The author's great grandparents, the Rev. Dr. Henry Charles Williams and Mother Daisy Franklin — Williams with nine of their ten children.

For the difference you make, with love

PaA~Pq8

6/17

Let Me Tell You Something

By Patience F. Rage

Let Me Tell You Something. Copyright ©2016 by Patience F. Rage. Published by**: P.F. Rage**

The story, *"Let Me Tell You Something"* is a work of oral history, collected by the author in her 30-year quest to document the history of her family.

"How I Got the Story," is an abbreviated version of a work of memoir written by the author and published in the Chestnut Hill Local *newspaper May 21, 2015 under the title, "Poignant Memories of Love and Loss at a Family Reunion."*

"Pauline Armstrong" was previously published by the City Paper *(May 2013 Philadelphia) as a runner-up winning entry in their annual short story contest.*

"Haagard" was previously published in B.Ma: Sonia Sanchez Literary Review, Drexel University Press, Fall 1998. Philadelphia.

ISBN 978-0-9982895-0-2

Manufactured in the United States of America

Cover Design: Nafessa Collins

Original Cover Painting: Commissioned by Patience Rage, author. Painted by Diane Keller (from a family photo taken in their North Philadelphia home).

~ Introduction ~

In this small collection, I offer readers a sampling of my work, which some say defies categorization. I will tell you that these five works include oral history, memoir, and short story. The piece, "Let Me Tell You Something," is based upon an interview with my great Uncle Charlie, who shared with me several stories of his long life.

Three stories relate a young girl's impressions of very different, very strong women.

"Haagard" relates the story of a woman coming through an abusive relationship. "Pauline Armstrong" is a story of an elderly woman who cared a lot about her neighborhood. Her neighbors didn't know much about her, though they saw her every day. And last, "A Bulldagger in the Family" is a coming of age story.

~Table of Contents~

~How I Got the Story~

How I Got the Story

Short of turning a trick, I would have done anything to get myself and my nine-year-old son to the family's reunion that summer. My interest in family history was pulling me south from Philadelphia. The reunion this year would take place in Savannah, Georgia, and I knew my Uncle Charlie, my grandfather's youngest brother, would be there.

I wanted to interview him for a project I had started of recording the family history—the life stories—of all the elders. Of my great grandparents' ten children, Charlie was the only one who didn't migrate north. I wanted to know why.

In 1985, you could still walk up to the counter at the airport, write a check, show your identification and get on a plane whether you had money or not. And that's exactly what I did. It was my son's first flight. Wee! Now, how we'd get back home was a whole other story, but I hadn't gotten that far yet.

Thank God the family reunion was being held in a hotel within walking distance of the Savannah Airport because my son and I had to walk there. I had 24 cents to my name. The two dimes and the four pennies were so shiny that I didn't feel broke.

It was my sweetheart of a mother in whose room we so uninvitedly crashed for that evening. The next day I found my Uncle Charlie in his room and told him about my family history project. He seemed interested and asked me to come back at 6 o'clock. I had a little cassette recorder but no tapes.

I went to family members from room to room knocking shamelessly for money to purchase cassette tapes for this interview. My mother's youngest sister, Aunt Almeda, was the one who gave me the money I needed.

I arrived on time at my uncle's room. Uncle Charlie had dressed up in a navy blue two-piece suit with a baby blue and white pin-striped shirt accented by a grey silk tie and handkerchief. There was a fresh red carnation in his left lapel and a tiny purple pin through the other. He directed me to a seat across from him and began sharing these stories and loving memories. What follows, "Let Me Tell You Something," is my account.

6

~Let Me Tell You Something~

Photo on previous page is a snapshot of Charlie,
courtesy of the author.

Let Me Tell You Something

They call me C. M. Williams.

My full name is Charlie Marcus Williams.

I was born 1917, the 16th of September.

Don't know how old I was but...one thing that happened and gone that I remember because it was so much commotion. Didn't know what it was all about till after I got grown. I was a li'l bit-a-sompnother.

I remember the commotion because it was my mother and my mother's cousins that were the ones jumping up raisin sand and all.

And it was suppose to had been when I made my first step. Lord, my Aunt Annie Lou beat my mother remembering that.

I went to the 11th grade at Boggs Academy, in Keysville, Burke County, Georgia.[1] And like kids are today, I was stupid.

Source: boggsrurallifecenter.mysite.com

In fact I figured, well, I ain't go be nothin but a farmer no how and I got enough education to be a farmer.

---

[1] The Boggs Academy continues into the 21st Century as the Boggs Rural Life Center. It was founded in 1906 by the Presbyterian Church and operated as a boarding school for African American children until 1986.

So I quit school, lied to my parents. Said, there
was no need in my goin' to school 'cause my
eyes bothered me, I can't see good.
That was the lie.
And that's why I say I was stupid.

Outta one thing my Daddy say he long to see,
one of his boys finish school and go to college.
And didn't not one of us do it.

I think, not because he was my daddy, I think
he was a hard man to be.

You see, he went to school long after he was
grown, married, and had a whole lotta children.

My daddy was the type of guy that was always reachin. Reachin', reachin', and reachin'. Reachin' for somethin' more.

He went to the Walker Baptist Institute in Augusta Georgia.

THE WALKER BAPTIST INSTITUTE, AUGUSTA, GA., FOUNDED BY
DR. CHARLES T. WALKER

Source: digitalcollections.nypl.org/items/510d47df-94bf-a3d9-e040-e00a18064a99 (Shomburg Center collection) [2]

---

[2] The Institute was founded in 1902 by Dr. Charles T. Walker.

Growing Up...

We didn't have no whole lot. But we always had
something. When a man and woman work hard
to raise ten children like they did us, and keep
them all together, well, just that within itself
is an accomplishment.

See, what we do, we all sit down, okay? I got
my opinion, Lumby got his. Mary got her
opinion and Louise got hers
and so on and so forth.

We got that. Now here's what I mean. As far as
any destructive argument or behavior, as of
today we don't do it. We don't do it because my
mother and father wouldn't allow it

Charlie with his family, he is second from left in back row. Rev. Dr. Henry Charles Williams, Charlie's father, is in the front row. Photo courtesy of the author.

One thing though that I have never as of this point yet forgiven my brother Henry for.

You see, we had what you call a Model T Ford.

Henry could drive a car and we couldn't.

And he wouldn't let us drive it.

I never will forget this.

I had some money. I had a nickel. I had to pay my
brother Henry a nickel to let me drive the car just
from bout here to where you're sitting.
That's right, just to drive that car. Yeah.

You know, in life, I've always wanted something
else, since I was a little kid.
I might have inherited some of that from my
daddy, because like I say, he was always reaching.
Reaching for something new.

Course, he didn't accomplish much materially.
But I have always put forth the effort to have.

I usta' get my fifteen cents, tie it up in a rag and
stick it in one of the cracks in the wall.
When I put that money there, I'd leave it there.
And when I left home I think I had three or four
dollars in change.

I was about fourteen or fifteen years old when I
served in the C. C. Camp.
This must have been 1934-35 in Keysville,
Burke County, Georgia.

The Civilian Conservation Corps was a federal
program that was created to help
the destitute people and what not.

They would take one child out a family.
It was something similar to Job Corps.
CCC sent me to Fort Benning Georgia.[3]

---

[3]Fort Benning had 4 separate CCC Camps located within its boundaries;
two were for whites, and two were for blacks.

Young men in a CCC Camp 1933. wtip.org/content/legacy-civilian-conservation-corps-part-3-0

We ain't do nothin really. Go to the park, cut
down all the weeds. We would plant them
Australian pine trees all along the roads there.
I was 16 and you know what I was doing? I was
cutting cross tie, yep cutting cross ties, and
making nine dollars a week.

See, what you do, or the way they do it—you had
to cut a tree down.

They had a special type of ax.

That was the fun part.

You could think 'bout anything, no bosses.

You just had to be careful.

Then when you cut it down,

you had to cut it oh so long.

Then you had to shave it down on each side.

You wouldn't finish it. But you got paid for what
you did. We'd be down in the mud sometimes.
Something in life I never will forget—I was in the
mud once and a leech got on me.
I never will forget it. It started to goin' in my skin.

It got started in and I caught the end of it to pull it
out and couldn't pull it out.
The only way I got it was with my fingernails by
digging my nails into it.

Well, I say, I'm not making much progress here.

So I came back home, stayed for a while and
in my opinion, wasn't making anything of myself.
It's got to be something better than this.

Again, I left home with three dollars on a freight
train. That's how I left home—hoboin' on a freight
train. I told one sister. I told my sister Lee.[4]

I didn't tell my father. I didn't tell my mother. If I
had told them they wouldn't want me to go.
See, the point is, I had decided that I was leaving
come hell or high water.

So rather than disobey them, I'd rather not give
them the chance to try to talk me out of it
or prevent me from going.
So that's why I didn't tell them.
I left home, went to Fort Pierce, Florida.

---

[4] Charlie's Sister Lee lives in Philadelphia, and recently celebrated her
103rd birthday.

That's the town where my brother,
Robert Willie, died.

I stayed in Fort Pierce maybe three weeks picking
oranges. From there I went to Fort Lauderdale.

I might have been a rich guy today if I would have
accepted what was offered to me.
I started to work there with a man who had a
farm. Lots of land he was farmin.
Well, at this particular time there wasn't many
young guys my age what could drive, see.

Like I said before, I had to pay my brother a nickel
to drive the car. So I had learned how to drive.

Now, this was an old man but he still
had all his stuff.
Now he usta have me pick up people driving them
to and from his farms.

What he wanted, we sat down and talked.
He wanted to all but retire.
He wanted to just turn everything over to
somebody. He wanted somebody what was
responsible. Somebody what's go keep
things going and all.

Well, I didn't have no doubt about if I could do it.
But I wasn't ready to do it yet, because see, I
hadn't gotten away from the farm long enough to,
say, get some of it outta me for a while.

So for that reason I couldn't accept.
So, I just kept moving right along.

Marriage and Family...

I was a young man when I married. We were
together for twenty-eight years.
I met Shug in Fort Lauderdale in 1938. Her
mother and father had passed.
She was living with her sista, and that's where I
married her out of, her sista's house.

Now, my wife's cousins were the type of people
that always wanted something from somebody.
But never put forth the effort
to accomplish anything. They would throw away
everything they got their hands on.

Well, I wouldn't do it. My wife wouldn't do it.

So they developed the idea that we thought
we were better than they were.
That wa'nt the point.

The point was I was not going to work seven days
a week, get paid, come home and say, Here.
See, that was the type of life they were livin' and I
wa'nt go live that type of life.

Shug (Francis) Williams, obituary photo.

Now, Shug, my wife, didn't know I had a piece of
land 'til I was fixin' to start building on it.
She didn't know til one week before.
I say to her, You know what?
She says, What?
I say, I'm go start building us a house.
She says, No!

I say, I'm not kidding; and started unfolding the
plan. I say, See there, this is the plan I got.
See, I have this, this way and that, that way.

She wa'nt too happy cause we owed
two or three hundred dollars.
She say, Let's wait until we outta debt.

I say, No, that's too long. I went right ahead
and did it.

See, what happened was when I was working and
building our house, I was using all my salary for
materials and thangs, and
we were living off of her salary.
Yeah, that's how that happened,
we lived off her salary.

Now, my wife had a brother,
which wa'nt worth a dime.
He had three children by a
woman in Jacksonville.
He'd put the children in this foster home
and that foster home.
Well, you know how these welfare people do.

The children started growing and they talked
about splitting them up.
Well, the twins, Frank and Frances,
begged them to get in touch
with their Aunt Shug in Miami.

So, they called us and set up an appointment.
Well, it was a decision that had to be made
after all the discussion.
The bottom line was, we would take the three
children and we would raise them.

May have been 10 years later, my wife got out of
bed with me on a Monday morning. She say, I'm
go fix me some oatmeal, do you want some.
I said, No, 'cause I didn't want to get outta bed.

See, I worked nights and she worked days.
So, I'm just getting' in.

She went on to fix the oatmeal. I heard her
messin' 'round and all.
After a while she called to me, say, I'm going now,
I'm leaving. She went out, got in her car
and took off.

Soon as I laid up there and went to sleep,
the phone rang. I say, Now who in the devil could
that be calling me this early in the morning?
But that's me, so I answered. It was the police.
He said, Mr. Williams? I say, Yeah.
He says, This is officer sompnother, say, I'm at the
corner of 7th and Ash Street.
Say, your wife is here and she's been in a li'l
accident, look like she hurt.

Well, I jumped outta bed into some clothes and
took off in my car.
When I got there and looked at her,
there was a drop of blood on her uniform bib
that had dried.

She say, Honey, I don't feel well.
I say, it's all right.
I called her doctor from that corner and
told him what happened.

He said, Get her to the hospital
as quickly as you can. Said, I'll meet you there.
So, I took her in my car.

See, I usta' work at Cedar's for three years before I
started driving buses.
I got on the expressway so when I got off,
I'd be right at Cedars, only a matter of minutes.

On the way, she was sitting next to me,
then laid her head on my lap.

When I take my foot from the accelerator to
brake, she says, What's the matter Charlie,
my head too heavy?
I say, No, your head ain't too heavy.
When I pulled up to the emergency room and saw
a couple of guys I knew out there,
I called to 'em, say, Whatshisname, brang me a
wheel chair, my wife sick.

Boy, I tell you, they brought out a wheelchair, had
told some of the nurses and all.
They rushed out there, grabbed her, wheeled her
in and were on her like flies to honey.
Put her on the table and started undressing her.
Soon as they laid her down, she died.
She was dead and there wa'nt nothing nobody
could do to help her in no kinda way.
But I was interested in why this thang
happened like it did.

So, I discussed it with her sista and
she agreed to let them 'form an autopsy.
And what the results were you see,
she was driving 'long and an artery burst and
leaked one drop of blood.
When it leaked, she blacked out and
then regained conscious.
And that's when the accident happened,
when she was out.

Said the vessel was weak to leak the one. And
when it burst, it flooded her brain.

The last thang my Shug said to me was, How
come you ain't let me walk in?

Charlie and Shug were together nearly 30 years until her death in 1970. Charlie lived another 30 years without her, and died in 2004.

~Haagard~

Haagard

She was the black sheep of the girls. Outright sassy and just as grown as she could be...is how they talked about her.

She was the only one of the three sisters who would come home from school unkempt and completely distracted. Her dress hem usually ripped out, rimmed glasses crooked with one eye cracked, scraped knees, hair all over her head.

Haagard is the one who was not afraid to speak her mind. Haagard is the one who would not turn her back on her father's romantic affairs. Haggard is the one whose jaw was broken at nine years old to keep her mouth shut.

Haagard, the momma's girl. She would fight anybody about her momma, even if she were their momma, too. Yet, she could not properly administer her mother's insulin.

Haagard was labeled a party girl in her mid-twenties. There are lots of photographs in family albums of her at the 31 Bar. It's where she retreats every night after work and all day weekends. She's always a little drunk and quick to pop her fingers.

Haagard has been cut and she has cut people. One of her hands is permanently disfigured as a result of one of her bar room brawls. She had two operations and a lot of therapy to get that pinky moving again. Her right ear had to be reattached long before Holyfield's. And this was behind some scrape she got into with this girl a few years younger than she.

People in Strawberry Mansion are still talking about that fight. My Aunt Haagard is full of fights and fun.

Anyway, the whole family went to this cabaret that a friend was giving at the Blue Horizon Ballroom. Haagard got down on the dance floor and started dancing and ...oh my god! First of all, she was dressed like a cat. It was New Year's Eve. Haagard's boyfriend was this thick, rough looking man we called James. The part of him that was bearable to the family was all the attention he paid to Haagard. No one had ever been around for her in that way. Not even her dead ex-husband. And how he died is a whole 'nother story.

So anyway, this boyfriend had come over to the house one morning just to say, hello. We were all in the kitchen of my grandmother's house when the bell rang. Haagard answered. The two of them stood in the vestibule like high school children staring into each other's eyes...mumbling.

Then, he left.

Haagard returned to the kitchen, wearing her famous grin. Everybody wanted to hear what was going on and she took her sweet ole time. Baby Sis went back to peeling yams. Papoose and Aunt Annie Mae went back to setting the dining room table, my mother, to making bacon and grits for Poppa, who had not come downstairs yet.

Me and my sister Mattie never stopped eating our Rice Krispies, ears to the bowls while all four eyes roamed the rooms. We giggled at the snorting, farting old lady on the living room couch.

Haagard speaks, "He just come by to tell me he love me." Everybody screamed at the same time and woke up grandmother on the couch. She sat up, half asleep and said, "If you talking behind my back, you talking to my crack," and went back to sleep. Me and my sister hit the floor laughing. The adults said something about grandmother being on a different medication, shushing one another and asking Haagard questions at the same time. "What did you say, what did you say to him, girl?"

Haagard grinning from ear to ear went back to plucking, washing and singeing the chickens. After a minute or two, Haagard pulled one hand from the sink, turned it backwards on the hip that had carried me and my sister. She turned halfway around and looked back at all of us looking at her and this is what she said, "I told him, uh, I love you too." Everybody screamed again, muffled though. This time we didn't wake up you-know-who.

So, about this cabaret we all went to. Three generations of us. That's how we do!

Well, these lovebirds must have had something to prove to one another.

Mr. I-love-you was on her so tight you would have thought he was her dress.

Well, no one was surprised when Auntie got possessed right along with that fool. She started doing this dance with her arms all up in the air and her rear end shaking. A crowd started to encircle her and she and this man went wild. The men were hollering and cheering her on. The louder the crowd the higher her arms went and the higher her arms, the higher the dress.

The crowd cheered. The family did not. Her boyfriend got down on his knees, in a drunken stupor, and begged her to stop doing that dance. All the people who stood around with cameras, no one took a picture.

The song ended – "Shotgun," by Junior Walker and the Allstars. The crowd dispersed, exposing Haagard and her boyfriend in the floor's center stumbling for stability. They looked like they had gone fifteen rounds with one another.

Haagard went from looking like a long, chic black cat in her body fitting mohair mini and them bad ass gold stilettos, to a sweaty, drunken four-eyed fool. Her man went to one end of the Blue Horizon and found he was at the wrong table, she followed. At our tables, her family and friends watched from afar. No one would help the two. By this time we were all in stitches.

Believe it or not, she and this man carried on like this for a couple of years, 'til she moved in with him. He thought he owned her and she wasn't even sitting around all day watching the soaps. She was bringing home the bacon. She was working just as hard in that hospital's laundry room as he was, if not harder. He got to beating on her after they got this house together and got it all fancily furnished with white carpet and said we couldn't come over cause the rug would get dirty. Yeah, he beat up on her and Aunt Haagard ain't never been no woman to let nobody beat up on her.

She had preached this stuff to her sisters who thought it was a natural part of being a woman to be beat up, mistreated, and screwed. That was why Haagard got into so many scrapes coming up. Plus, she had gotten a lot of practice from her own daddy who had to break her jaw to keep her mouth shut. He was mean as a snake and she stood her sweet ground with him. James beat her so bad in and out of their plush home, the neighbors cried.

They say she ran out of the house. They heard the screams. He followed her in his underwear. They say he jumped on her back, knocked her to the ground. They say he straddled her and began beating her all in her head.

One woman said the blood gushed from her ear, that he knocked her eyeglasses off and crushed them. Without her glasses, Haagard is the 'she' version of Mr. Magoo.

They say she flipped that wrist that she was famous for, grabbed his already spread balls and twisted them things like she was opening a can of Pillsbury biscuits. He let go. She jumped up, ran, and ain't never looked back.

My mother and her other sisters keep telling her to go back and get her things. Haagard tells them she can get more things, just like she got what she left there. But she cannot get another life.

One of her sisters, whose nose was broken by her husband twice in nine months, told Haagard, "It would have had to been a bear up in there to make me leave all the shit I done worked for all these years, huh!"

Haagard said, No! and she meant it.

~Pauline Armstrong~

48

Pauline Armstrong

I had not seen her for a few days, so I tiptoed to her apartment on the third floor and peeked through the keyhole. She was laid out on the sofa, face up. Flies were swarming around her head. Hands folded deliberately across her stomach. She smiled. She had no children or family anyone knew to call.

Momma told the police she had a first cousin somewhere in New Jersey. For her, I wish she had been taken out with a little more dignity, because I knew how she was. She would have had a fit at the way these men were carrying her out of the house. All bunched up and poor looking. It wasn't that she would have minded dying. But she would have dressed up.

Probably with her fox fur collar. Mrs. Armstrong would have wanted one of those orange and white ambulances to take her away. No sirens, for God's sake. She was a proud woman. So, to see the police bring her out half covered and throw her in the back of a meat wagon made something in me scream.

She was the only person on the block that could talk about yo' mama and get away with it. For spitting on the sidewalk, she told Dwayne from next door that he didn't have the manners of a dog because his mother didn't. Dwayne ran in the house to tell his mother what the old woman had said about her.

In two seconds flat, Miss Corlee filled the doorway, covering the part of her mouth where teeth were lost. In the direction of the old woman she shouted, "Fuck that half white bitch. She ain't got no momma, and ugly as she is, probably ain't never had one...hell she probably wa'nt never even born, huh."

But the old woman never cared who said what about her. She never heard anyone talk but herself.

There was a way she had of signifying when an opened bag was left on the sidewalk for trash. She would not say a word to the person who put the trash out. She would go to the nearest neighbor, twitching her head in the direction of the bag, "Well what you think of that?" Never expecting an answer from the person to whom she spoke.

Fist on her hips, "See, folks couldn't leave trash all over the street when I first come here. Did, they'd get a fine so fast they wouldn't see it coming. But you know, they grow 'em like that now...uh huh."

In a bad broken strut she walks up the street. On her long faded skirt, a pocket is sewn to cradle her Pall Malls, her handkerchief and keys. She was a small bow legged woman never weighed a hundred pounds and smoked like a champ.

We called her Filter King because by the time she finished rolling the thing from one side of her mouth to the other, the wet end meets the fire end halfway down, and simmers out every time. But you could not tell her that. She thought she was smoking the whole thing.

There was a dog in the neighborhood that had come from somewhere, that was anybody's guess. The women called her "Lady," and I think it was because she sat around and waited to be fed and had litter after litter after litter. Sometimes her pups lived. Most times, no. The charred body of one of her pups was found hanging from its neck in Tina's basement. Anyway, Lady is who the old woman compared the young girls in the neighborhood to.

Summer days on 17th and Jefferson Street, before the sun came to our side of the street, Mrs. Armstrong is out with her bucket, scrub brush, brooms and rags to begin her daily ritual. Depending on her mood, she'd scrub the steps next door, Miss Corlee fussing the entire time. Then she'd sweep all the way to the corner stopping many times to straighten her back.

After she swept, she'd pull up weeds in cracks along the curb. Then, carefully bag the trash and carry it to Freedman's dumpster, on the corner. When her work was done, she didn't want a soul sitting on them steps, and whoever did became the target of her verbal abuse for the rest of the day. The block did look completely different when she finished.

But one day in particular, we sat on them steps and waited for the old woman to be done. We saw her coming up the street, we sat and stared straight ahead and tried not to burst into laughter.

Here she comes. She stops in front of the steps she's just scrubbed. Exhausted, bucket, mop and broom in one hand, the other on her hip. At four teenagers sprawled out on her steps, she says, "Your asses can find these steps soon as I've scrubbed 'em but nobody can find your asses to scrub 'em. Get your li'l dirty asses up.

She plops her tired body down on the steps and we all scatter. "Eeeeww, she touched you," somebody screamed.

Cheryl had this douche bag hose that had been floating through the neighborhood for days, like an old shoe or broken skate. But this hose we used as a microphone. To the old woman, Cheryl sang,

Betcha didn't know that my knees get weak, when I'm near you baby!

Betcha didn't know that it's hard to speak, when I'm near you baby

Cheryl pointed at the old woman,

Betcha didn't know that my heart beats fast...

"You children don't have the manners of a damn dog," the old woman puffed. We thanked her, bowing and laughing over newly scrubbed steps and parked cars.

Of all the years my family has lived on the first floor of this apartment house, no one has ever visited the old woman. Sam, the rent man and his helper, Mr. Dee, were the only ones to go upstairs.

Well, my brother used to go up there after he came home from Vietnam. But that's a whole other story.

Mrs. Armstrong would make her way to Progress Plaza, the third of every month to cash her check and to make her stop at the State store. She could almost be timed to turn the corner two hours later...tipsy...and proud.

And on Sundays she dresses for Jesus. In a fitted suit that accents her fallen figure. A diaper pin holds the body of a little fox collar close to her lapel, while the head hangs piercing eyes over her heart.

Consistently she pat-taps at her hair as though she may lose a strand. And if ever she could stand up straight in her run over shoes, surely she'd fall over backwards. A long time ago she was fine. A time ago lost. Her native red skin was now blotched and unsightly. Tired hazel eyes struggle through cataracts. She cannot see change.

The last time I saw her, she came downstairs and told my mother that her husband had not been to see her and could mom give her a little bit of food. A plate of Mom's food steamed as I carried it to the stairs for the old woman who shuffled behind me carrying a jar of lemonade. She seemed to be shrinking, becoming less important.

I had not seen her for a few days, so I tiptoed to her apartment on the third floor and peeked through the keyhole. She was laid out on the sofa. Flies were swarming her face. She lay in peace.

~ A Bulldagger in the Family~

A Bulldagger in the Family

I didn't know what a bulldagger was but I sure
wanted to be one by the time I was eight years
old. I wanted to be just like Katherine Hicks --
mostly because of the commotion she stirred
among the women in the family, just in her
mere appearance.

The fun they had imitating her gestures, the
way she strolled and dragged that one leg, the
way she spoke with a cigarette hanging out of
one side of her mouth. They mocked her style
of dress and the women she 'ran' with.

Katherine was a tall, light-skinned woman with
a diamond-shaped face, eyes set deep in the
bone under arched eyebrows. Katherine wore a
process styled like Elvis Presley with that hunk
of hair in the front and it was a reddish brown.

Her nose was thin and straight, full lipstick lips parted exposing paint-white teeth and the friendliest lopsided grin.

One Sunday morning as we were all in the kitchen getting ready for church, we could hear Auntie Haagard coming downstairs. She came in, with a cigarette dangling from the side of her mouth, strutting across the kitchen floor dragging one leg. Well, my aunties hit the floor laughing. They laughed so hard their sides ached.

Katherine was the only daughter of Mr. and Mrs. Hicks who lived next door to my grandparents. She was in her mid- to late twenties and wreaked of passion, sensuality, and a tad of old spice. She always wore men's clothing, from head to toe. There were never exceptions.

They say Katherine wore a breast band. I wondered what it was, how it worked and how do I get one?

What did it mean that she carried her wallet in the hip pocket of her sharkskins? Or that her shirts were starched, high-boy collars? Or that her black leather belt had the initials 'K' and 'H' as a buckle? What did it all mean? I did know what gut-wrenching laughter it brought to the women in my family when one of them did a Katherine impression.

There was no one anywhere like her. All that was certain was that, in some sneaky kind of way, women wanted her time, attention or just to be noticed by her.

My mother and her sisters would break their necks to get a look at her every time they heard the Hicks' front door open or shut. One of them would run to the window and peek through the blinds to see if it was Katherine. And if so, the person at the blinds would give the 'come look' hand gesture. Boy oh boy did I want to be like Katherine Hicks.

She worked where almost everybody worked, Bayunks Cigar Factory. Lots of people in our neighborhood worked there. My aunt Haagard and my uncle John Henry worked there too.

Katherine also worked weekends at the 31 Bar just around the corner and across the street from the drug store. I went to the drug store a lot for Grand momma and I listened to everything everybody said – and I listened to the things they didn't say.

The feeling of another person's pain shivered

through me when I heard the women talking of the beating. "She ain't had no business up in that man's face in the first place," and "She ain't no man, neva was and neva will be," and "Well, if you go act like a man, may's well expect to be treated like one, huh," or "What she expect?" and "She should've kept her mouth shut and stayed in her place," and "I bet she go keep it shut now."

They all laughed in a way that wasn't real, almost like they didn't believe themselves.

I knew they were all lying and they didn't really feel that way. I could tell they thought they were supposed to act and say what they were saying. I just didn't know why.

A few days later I saw Katherine with my own eyes, arm in arm with Mr. and Mrs. Hicks, bringing her home from the hospital. She was different. Her jaw wired shut the size of an apple and both arms in casts. Her hair combed straight back showed where a patch had been cut away just above her ear to allow the stitches.

I ran out to the porch to say hi to her and she never looked my way. I don't think she knew I was there. I cried for three days.

It is the summer of 1962, I am now ten years old, and Katherine is finally able to talk again. Her smile is gone as well as most teeth. I heard someone say she has nerve damage in her wrist and can't wrap cigars anymore at Bayunks. She is really skinny now and drinks a lot of beer.

She never went back to work at the 31 Bar, she just goes there.

Most Friday evenings now, a heavy set white woman in a sky blue Cadillac convertible comes to pick her up. It is like clockwork.

The woman never gets out of the car, the top is always down and we only ever see the driver from the waist up. It's as though she had no legs. Peggy-was-her-name would pull up, blow the horn, and then we saw Katherine running out. Just that quickly she'd be gone until Sunday night.

One Sunday around dusk I was sitting on the front steps when Peggy's car pulled up and dropped Katherine off after saying good night the way they do: first the convertible top goes up very slowly and covers the two of them. Then it takes a few minutes for Katherine to get out.

That particular evening, when she turned away from the car and saw me on the steps, she smiled big like she always did when seeing me and said, "Hi." She was the only grownup that I knew who liked me. "Hey young lady, whatcha doing sitting out here all by yourself witch ya lips poked out, huh?" I said, Hi back to her and asked her did she hear about my friend.

"Yesterday, Carmen...do you know my best friend Carmen that lives down the street next door to Tuggie and his family? Me and her were in the relays together. One year she beat me and then the next year I beat her. That's why we were best friends because both of us can run really fast and neither one of us could beat the other running."

Not giving Katherine a chance to answer, "She fell, my friend Carmen fell down the steps

Friday and hit her head and the ambulance came and took her to the hospital. They took her to the same hospital me and her were both born in."

I kept right on talking, "Carmen was in a coma yesterday and they say she was still in a coma today and it was way, way, way, too much pressure on her brain and she told her mother it was hurting too bad and she was tired and wanted to go to sleep and her mother told her she could go to sleep if she was too tired to stay woke and she went to sleep and she never woke back up...she died.

"She died just like that. I miss her. Did you see President Kennedy when he was on Ridge Avenue? He white, I saw him. Do you want to play some jacks?" "Sure Kid," Katherine said.

We played jacks and I told her all about Carmen and me and the time we raced from my house to school without stopping. "One time I beat Carmen up and two times she beat me up and we was still the best friends ever...can you still be best friends with somebody after they die?

"One time we wanted to be blood sisters and she got a safety pin and we poked a hole in her thumb and squeezed the blood out and then we did mine and then we put our thumbs together and squeezed 'em and now we blood sisters. Can we still be blood sisters if she died?"

"Sure you can, kid, you'll always be best friends." Katherine and I played jacks and talked until Momma called me in the house for my bath.

I remember the day I was straddling the banisters between the Hicks' and my grandparent's house when Peggy pulled up and blew the horn. This time when Katherine came out of the house she was carrying a small suitcase. I asked her where she was going and she said, 'Young lady," – I liked it when she called me 'young lady' – "I'm going to Washington D.C., where every Negro in America should be going, I'm going to the Freedom March to march with the King. See you later, be a good girl."

When the evening news came on and I heard the reports of the March on Washington and saw all the people, I looked really hard for Katherine and Peggy.

It was the summer of 1963 and at eleven years old I had already been beaten, raped and spat on, but still I was determined to be a doctor, a lawyer or a school teacher.

That was the summer I took a pair of black pants that my brother had outgrown and claimed them as mine. I cut the legs off and made myself a pair of shorts.

I wore these cut-offs every single day after school. I wore these pants to the point my family got concerned. What the concern was I was not certain. My grandmother was totally disgusted with me. She spoke to my mother and demanded that my mother make me stop wearing the pants.

I didn't know this at the time, but the pants gave me a way to feel protected. I wore them because they were comfortable. I had pockets for the first time and could put everything in my pockets. And I did.

I carried my candy, rubber bands, a couple of cats' eye marbles, a nickel, and my sister Patty's doll baby head that I promised to fix.

It was so much fun having those pants with deep pockets. I did not understand my family's meanness toward me for wearing the pants. I was being accused of something I knew nothing about, and I knew I was innocent.

I could hardly wait to get home from school to jump into my pants, get my homework and chores over with and zip, zip, zip my sense of freedom and independence. I felt like I had special powers. To run, jump and play was so much easier in pants. What were the adults in my life so worried about? My aunties and my mean old grandmother got on my nerves all the time and I didn't like any of them.

My Aunt Haagard is getting married at our house to Mr. James Brown. His family owns the barber shop around the corner. Momma is in the wedding and takes a lot of time to make certain my hair is done and my clothes are laid out on the bed.

My dress is a pinkish thing with a bow around the waist, puffy sleeves and a crinoline beside it. Yuck! I didn't refuse to wear the dress. I just knew I didn't want to. Plus it was the dress I wouldn't wear for Easter.

As it turns out everyone was so busy getting the final touches done that I practically went unnoticed. Every once in a while one of my aunts would say in passing, "Girl, get upstairs and get dressed." And I'd say, "Yes Ma'am." I really meant to put that dress on, but I never got around to it. There is one wedding picture floating around the family where I stuck my head in. I was wearing a No. 2 pencil behind my ear, and showed the biggest smile ever.

It was Uncle Johnny who first called me a bulldagger. I later realized he called it the way the family saw it and whispered it.

Cynthia, my cousin, and I were sitting on the floor playing jacks. No other adult was home. Johnny got a blanket and pretended to be a matador moving from side-to-side with the blanket in front of him.

He called out to me to charge the blanket, "Here bully, bully, bully, bully, bulldagger!"

You a Bulldagger if ever I saw one. Did you grow a dick yet?"

This was the first heartbreak I'd ever felt. I didn't have words for the shame and embarrassment I felt in front of my closest cousin. I remember we stopped playing together so much after that.

And I still did not understand everyone's disdain for me and these pants. I was being accused of being something I knew nothing about. What is a bulldagger? What does any of this mean?

One afternoon I came home from school full of energy and pride, god only knows where I got it from. I ran to the third floor to jump into my power pants. I got to my room and before I stepped over the threshold I could see my pants on top of the trash can cut to shreds.

Oh my god! It took a minute for the shock to give way to the hurt. No one ever explained anything to me. There were no apologies.
By the time I was fourteen years old all I could think about was kissing Edna Canning. She had lips like a black girl, full and moist. I wanted to kiss her lips, not Edna. I didn't know if that could happen or not, so I tried it – and she was horrified. What made her think that kissing another girl was wrong? I just didn't understand it.

A year after Edna, I got the hardest lesson of all. When I arrived home from school one afternoon, Momma told me that my friend Katherine's body was found in the alley behind the 31 bar. The evening news said her throat had been deeply slashed. And her chest bore 76 stab wounds. I was stunned, beyond despair. Yet, somehow for me, in that moment, it came together and I understood everything.

~ Acknowledgements ~

For my love and life partner Susan Christian, editor and assistant manager to this project. For all the good that happens in my life, because you and I work together sharing our lives and love.

For Sanaz R. Labafzadeh, my partner for life, who loves the "Cookie Jones" in me...

For Dr. Constance Garcia-Barrio, it was your years of time, attention, friendship, patience and rewrites that helped me earn my Goddard degree.

For my dear friend Linda Hanna with whom I go fishing... to throw them back LOL.

For my great grandparents, Rev. Dr. Henry Charles Williams and Mother Daisy Franklin Williams (who have been in my life all my life) and all of their ten children, the eldest being my grandfather.

For my grandparents, Deacon Eugene Henry Williams and Sister Almeda Flintall Williams, who had seven children including my mother, Mary.

A special appreciation and love to my parents, Curtis Fields and Mary Pearl Williams Fields who to this minute are my favorite storytellers.

A salute to my brilliant older brother Larry (Spec 4, 82nd Airborne), who served in the Vietnam War at age 18, and who died at 41, a casualty of wartime drug addiction. He was the better writer.

For my Aunt Almeda Eiland: all my recorded interviews of elders and ancestors were made possible by the $10 you gave me at the family reunion to buy cassette tapes. With those tapes, I recorded my interviews with my Uncle Charlie (included in this collection. Thanks Auntie!

This could be looked at as name dropping but I'm thinking it's more like giving praise to the many teachers who have paved a way for me.

For Dr. Sonia Sanchez, thank you for all the community workshops and readings. Thank you for allowing me to sit in on your Temple University writing classes. Thank you for helping me win the Larry Neal cultural award, and for bringing us James Baldwin, Dr. Margaret Walker, E. Ethelbert Miller, and

Gwendolyn Brooks, to name a few. You continue to inspire me.

Thank you to Audre Lorde, Nikky Finney, Jan Clausen and Paula Gunn Allen. And finally, Toni Cade Bambara—teacher, neighbor and friend. Hey Toni, remember that night I gave you a ride to Scribe? We were running late. I said, "Oh my God, look at all this traffic." You said, "I don't see traffic, I see buffalo." Rest in peace my sister.

I appreciate the Leeway Foundation for the grant that I used to buy new digital recording equipment.

For my beloved son, Charles McLaurin II, from whom I learned that nurturing a story is like nurturing a child. I love being your mother.

April 20, 2017

My dear, dear sister Nafessa, my project manager,

Your knowledge, skill, spirit, patience and grace made this publication possible.

Look at what we've done, in spite of the challenges. Turns out nothing can stop us.

We didn't start out knowing that Bill would be diagnosed with cancer and not one round of inpatient chemo, no no no – two rounds.

I mean, didn't we go from sitting at the dining room table finishing up this project to your getting the fateful call from your husband? You rushed home to get him to the hospital and this project was slowed down. Within 48 hours he was hooked up to an IV feeding him chemo.

It is what it is, you would say. You were at the hospital full time for two months, and still found time to take the next steps with this project. You were parenting three teenagers alone as Bill worked on his healing. And still you managed to help move this project along.

You are awesome children. Thank you Billie, thank you Isaiah and thank you Elijah for following the path your mother blazed for you.

I appreciate beyond measure the ways you have been willing to continue with the project in spite of those roadblocks and the ones I have also thrown at you. You are amazing.

Love, Patience

~ About the Author ~

Patience Rage was born in Philadelphia, the first and only daughter of her southern-born, working class parents. She has nine siblings, and all were raised by their (most of the time) single mother in multi-generational homes in the Strawberry Mansion section of North Philadelphia. Because the family moved a lot, Patience attended a dozen different schools. She describes her family as a bunch of hard workers deeply engaged in the struggle.

Patience knew early on she wanted to tell stories—hers is a family of storytellers. She remembers her great-grandfather, from the pulpit, telling stories every Sunday to thunderous response. And her 99-year-old great-grandmother telling her the story of her first beating by her father. And her mother, who through her own stories, taught her the difference between a story and a lie. Her father told unbelievable stories (or were they lies?) of how he left the South—stories that sent the author South on a journey toward self-discovery and love.

Patience is in the first generation born in the North, and many of her stories reflect that migration. Who Hoo!

~ Also by Patience F. Rage ~

"Better Than," collected in
<u>Class Action</u>: Stories from across Our
Economic Divide. Cornell University Press.

<u>Incest Journals</u>
Memoir. Self-published.

"Jim Crow Eat Your Heart Out."
Article. *Off Our Backs* magazine.

"Poignant Memories of Love and Loss at
Family Reunion." Memoir. Published in
Chestnut Hill Local.

"'Snow Pudding' Is Poor Folks' Ice Cream."
Memoir. Published in *Chestnut Hill Local.*

"When You Run Up on One of Them Mean
Crackahs, Ya Gotta Not Care If You
Live or Die." Oral history.
Published in *Apiary Magazine.*

"One Heart"
A gift to the author from her granddaughter, Ameerah McKnight.

Made in the USA
Middletown, DE
23 May 2017